page 3

page 6

page 15

page 30-31

Leap Ahead Workbook

English

Home learning made fun

d	t	c	a	t	f
o	s	h	y	b	g
g	k	u	a	w	o
b	m	w	t	r	a
r	a	b	b	i	t
s	v	e	p	o	m

cat

goat

dog

rabbit

igloobooks

About Me

Read the instructions and draw a picture in each box.

This is me:

This is my family:

This is my home:

Sticker Match

Read each word out loud. Then, find the matching sticker.
The first two have been done for you.

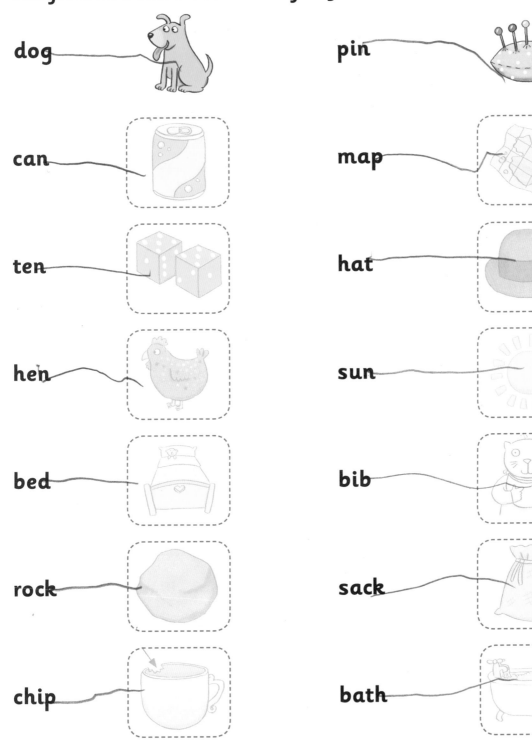

dog

pin

can

map

ten

hat

hen

sun

bed

bib

rock

sack

chip

bath

3

The Witch's Washing

Find the letters of the alphabet floating in the cauldron and write them in the correct order on the witch's washing line. Some have been done for you.

PARENT TIP: Although your child will recognise most letters by now, it is useful for them to remember what order they come in so that they can start to use dictionaries and indexes.

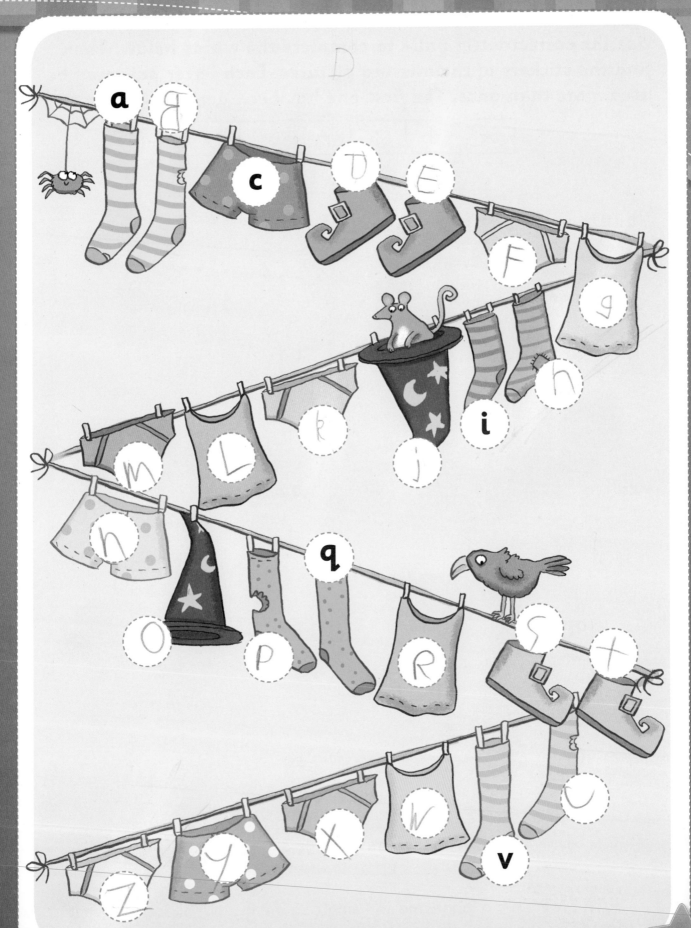

Two Letters, One Sound

Use the correct letter pairs to complete the words below. Then find the stickers of the missing pictures. Each letter pair may be used more than once. The first one has been done for you.

| zz | ll | sh | th | ss | ck |

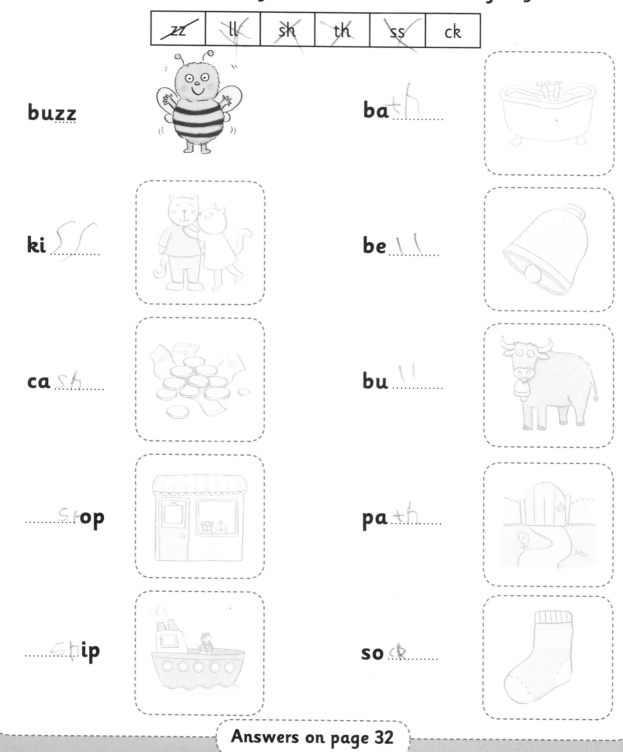

bu<u>zz</u>

ba<u>th</u>

ki <u>ss</u>

be <u>ll</u>

ca <u>sh</u>

bu <u>ll</u>

<u>sh</u>op

pa <u>th</u>

<u>sh</u>ip

so <u>ck</u>

Answers on page 32

PARENT TIP: A 'phoneme' is a single sound in a word. Sometimes it is made by one letter, e.g. the 'p' in 'pot', and sometimes it is made by two or more letters, e.g. the 's' sound in 'fuss' or the 'th' in 'bath'.

Tricky Letters

Some words with tricky letters are hiding in the picture below. See if you can find them, then choose the correct letters from the box to complete each label.

qu	x	y	z

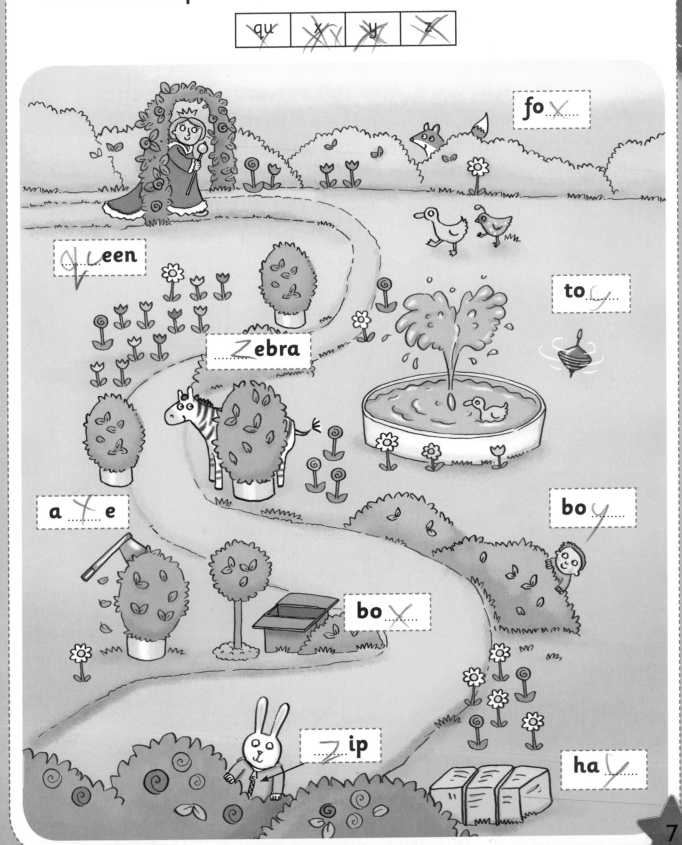

fo x

queen

to y

zebra

a x e

bo y

bo x

zip

ha y

A Trip to the Zoo

Megan's class has been on a trip to the zoo. Read Megan's report. Then write numbers in the circles to show the order the class visited each place. The first one is done for you.

Our trip to the zoo

We started by the cafe. We walked towards the monkeys. Then, we turned left towards the giraffes. We went around the hippos and then turned right towards the gorillas. The last animals we saw were the elephants. Afterwards we had an ice cream at the ice cream van. Then we got on the bus and went home.

1 2 3 4 5 6 7 8 9 10

Answers on page 32

Robot Names

Rearrange the letters in these robot names to make words. Draw a line to match each robot up to the correct word. The first one has been done for you.

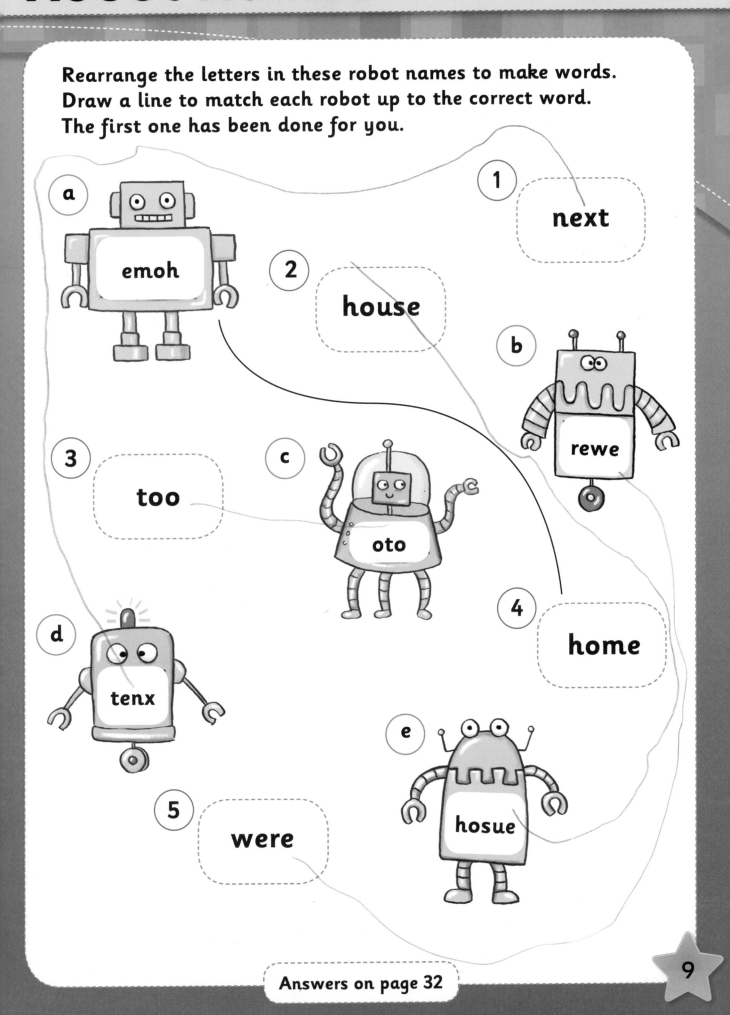

a emoh

1 next

2 house

b rewe

3 too

c oto

4 home

d tenx

e hosue

5 were

Answers on page 32

Magic Spellings

Some of the vowels have dropped out of the magician's spell book! Choose the correct vowels to complete the words. The five vowels are listed in the box below to help you.

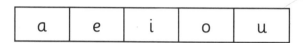

a	e	i	o	u

A spell to put a fr_o_g in your sister's b_a_th.

A s_i_lly tr_i_ck to play on your m_u_m.

How to make a c_u_t turn p_i_nk.

These items are missing the last two letters in their names. Can you add either 'ng' or 'nk' in the correct places? The first one has been done for you.

si_nk_

wi_ng_

si_ng_

i_nk_

PARENT TIP: Explain to your child that the letter 'y' sometimes sounds like a vowel, such as in the word 'sky', but because the sound it most often makes is the 'y' as in 'yellow', it isn't referred to as one.

Guess Who?

Read each description, then look at the pictures.
Draw lines to match each description to the right person.

a
This person has not got black hair. He has a red hat. He has a blue jumper and he has got a book in his hands. His name is Tom.

b
This girl has got a pink dress. She has a teddy in a red bag. Her name is Becky.

2

3

c
This man has black hair. He works in a bank. He has to dress smartly every day. He helps a lot of people. His name is Sunil.

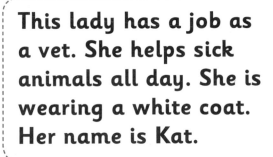

d
This lady has a job as a vet. She helps sick animals all day. She is wearing a white coat. Her name is Kat.

4

Answers on page 32

Busy Toyshop

Can you spot all of the things in the box on the right in the toyshop? When you find them, list each word under the correct spelling pattern. The first ones have been done for you.

Monday
Tuesday
Wednesday
Thursday
Friday
Saturday
Sunday

free

ai	oa	ee
rail	**coat**	**feet**
TRAIN	boat	TEETH
PLAIN	Con	free
		chees

feet, teeth, boat, coat, jeep, train, rain, stain, goat, free, throat, cheese, tree, road, toad, foal, week, sail, tail, rail, sweet

13

Missing Letters

Add the missing letters to these words that you found on the previous page. The first one has been done for you.

f̲e̲e̲t	c .... t	g .... t
t .... th	tr .... n	s l
t .... d	st .... n	sw .... t

Can you write some short sentences using some of the words above?

1. **I have big f̲e̲e̲t̲ and little hands.**

2. ....

   ....

3. ....

   ....

4. ....

   ....

5. ....

   ....

6. ....

   ....

7. ....

     ....

Party Time!

Write the missing capital letters beneath the lower case letters to fill in the spaces on the bunting. Then, decorate the page with party stickers from your sticker sheet.

Me First

Look at each of these pictures and complete the missing words using the letters in the box. Which nouns need a capital letter?

c	J	F	t	S	b

cup   .... ree   .... ally

.... ack   .... ido   .... ox

Sentences always start with a capital letter. Which of the following are sentences? Fill in the missing letters, using capital letters at the start of any full sentences.

1. ......y dad's dog is called Fido.

2. ......potty dog

3. ......y family

4. ......his is my car.

Answers on page 32

PARENT TIP: Explain to your child that a noun is another name for an object or thing. A common noun is an everyday object and proper nouns describe just one thing or person. Proper nouns, e.g. people's names, always begin with a capital letter.

Stop at the Red Light

A full stop is the mark that we use to show that a sentence has finished. Read the story below. Add any full stops that you think are missing.

Mac is as fast as any car in town. He is as speedy as a train

Mac wants a race He asks Bus Bus says yes.

Mac and Bus are at the start The flag waves, "Go!"

Mac is fast Bus is last, but at the end of the street the lights are red

The lights are broken. No one can go

The broken light means they both win.

Answers on page 32

Adding Apostrophes

Match each of these words with apostrophes below to its long version.

I'll	We will
He'll	I will
We'll	He will
They'll	She will
She'll	They will

Choose which word from the box should go in each sentence.

I'll	she'll	we'll	he'll

If we don't hurry up, ... be late.

I am going out now, but .... see you later.

When Mum comes, ... give us our lunch.

Uncle Fred has funny hats. Which one do you think .... be wearing today?

Answers on page 32

Circus Syllables

Syllables are like beats within words, e.g. ti–ger. Read these words out loud and write dots underneath to show how many syllables are in each word. The first one has been done for you.

silly
● ●

acrobat

ringmaster

swing

terrible

fantastic

fuzzy

dog

clown

lion

monkey

juggle

horse

children

night

trick

jump

Answers on page 32

Time for a Puzzle

Which letters from the box are missing from the clues below? Write each word that you complete in the crossword. One has been done for you.

or	ar	oo

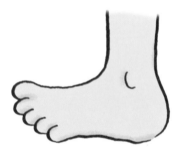

Across

1. The b _ _ n is red.

3. **Look** over there!

5. It's time to st _ _ t work.

6. It is too f _ _ to run.

7. I hurt my f _ _ t on the beach.

Down

1. Can you find my b _ _ k?

2. This dress is too sh _ _ t.

4. It is a shiny st _ _.

5. Is it the right s _ _ t of cheese?

6. Is this f _ _ me?

Answers on page 32

Remember, Remember

Read these words and try to remember how they are spelt. Write them on a separate piece of paper. How did you do?

going	began	think	things
food	fast	again	bear
wanted	these	first	boy
other	play	thought	magic
shouted	long	where	would
never	cried	before	night
mouse	boy	been	door
much	good	small	found
there	some	down	back
asked	can't	said	they

21

I Spy Spellings

Play I Spy in this fun beach scene, using the phonemes in the boxes below. For example, "I spy with my little eye, something with an 'air' sound." Take it in turns to ask and answer. When you find each item, write it under the correct phoneme at the bottom.

ar	**air**	**ee**
shark		feet
		chets

You should be able to find all of these items.
What else can you spot?

chair, coat, tears, summer, spear, soap, butter, tart,
cheese, mother, start, pair, father, sneeze, star, boat, cart,
feet, sheet, hammer

oa	er	ear
Boat		

Consonant or Vowel?

Follow the key and colour the grid. What picture can you see when all the squares are coloured?

vowel =

consonant =

q	w	r	t	y	p	s	d	f	g	h	j
d	s	z	x	c	v	b	n	i	m	l	k
f	g	h	j	k	l	p	y	o	t	r	w
h	g	k	l	p	y	t	r	a	i	w	q
f	d	s	q	w	r	t	y	o	o	p	y
q	a	e	i	u	i	a	u	u	e	i	t
w	a	o	u	o	e	i	o	e	a	o	r
r	m	n	b	v	c	x	q	o	e	s	d
t	y	p	y	t	r	w	q	e	u	z	x
f	g	h	j	k	l	m	n	a	b	v	c
d	s	q	w	r	t	y	p	i	l	j	h
f	l	k	h	v	m	b	b	c	d	f	g

Answer on page 32

PARENT TIP: Explain to your child that vowels are the letters 'a', 'e', 'i', 'o' and 'u'. All the other letters of the alphabet are consonants.

Word Score

Use a separate piece of paper to play this word game. Make words by picking two consonant letter tiles and one vowel combination. Add up the points on each tile to make a score for each word. What's your highest scoring word?

b 2

t 1

s 1

c 3

n 1

g 2

m 2

k 3

f 3

x 5

l 2

Example: b u t = 3 points, f ee t = 4 points, b o x = 7 points

o   ee   oa   u   oo   ar

Punctuation

Not all sentences end in full stops. Some use question marks or exclamation marks.

Look at these examples:

Would you like a drink?

Don't look!

Now add the correct punctuation to the end of these sentences.

1. **Do you have a hat** ....

2. **Can I have a sandwich** ....

3. **No** ....

4. **What do you want** ....

5. **It's a trick** ....

6. **What a mess** ....

7. **How does it work** ....

8. **Is it his or hers** ....

Answers on page 32

If I Was a Pirate...

If you were a pirate, what would your pirate name be?

Pirate name ....

Who would your shipmates be?

My shipmates ....

....

What would your ship be called?

The Good Ship ....

Where would you go for your first pirate adventure?

....

....

What would happen?

....

....

....

....

....

....

PARENT TIP: Make-believe is a great way to develop children's creativity and vocabulary, too. Talk about your child's ideas and let them grow!

27

Be the Author

Look at the pictures below and write a sentence under each picture to make a story. Draw the last picture yourself and make up the ending.

The Escape

1

Jess the cat was fed up. She decided to run away.

2

....
....

3

....
....

4

....
....

5

....

....

....

6

....

....

....

7

....

....

....

8

....

....

....

29

Help the Farmer

Farmer Brown wants to rearrange his farm. Help him by using the words in the box to label each area. Use stickers from the sticker sheet to finish the farm.

farm

sheep, cows, goats, ~~farm~~, barn, farmer's house, pigs, horses, hens, geese, ducks, tractor, shed, pond

Answers

Page 6: Two Letters, One Sound
bu<u>zz</u>, ba<u>th</u>, ki<u>ss</u>, be<u>ll</u>, ca<u>sh</u>, bu<u>ll</u>, <u>sh</u>op, pa<u>th</u>, <u>sh</u>ip, so<u>ck</u>.

Page 8: A Trip to the Zoo

Page 9: Robot Names
a – 4, b – 5, c – 3, d – 1, e – 2

Page 11: Guess Who?
a – 3, b – 4, c – 1, d – 2

Page 16: Me First
cup, tree, Sally, Jack, Fido, box.
Sally, Jack and Fido need capital letters.
<u>M</u>y dad has a dog called Fido. – <u>s</u>potty dog – <u>m</u>y family – <u>T</u>his is my car.

Page 17: Stop at the Red Light
Mac is as fast as any car in town.
He is as speedy as a train<u>.</u>
Mac wants a race<u>.</u> He asks Bus<u>.</u>
Bus says yes.
Mac and Bus are at the start<u>.</u>
The flag waves, "Go!"
Mac is fast<u>.</u> Bus is last, but at the end of the street the lights are red<u>.</u>
The lights are broken.
No one can go<u>.</u>
The broken light means they both win.

Page 18: Adding Apostrophes
I'll – I will, He'll – He will, We'll – We will, They'll – They will, She'll – She will.
(The following answers may vary) If we don't hurry up, <u>we'll</u> be late. I am going out now, but <u>I'll</u> see you later. When Mum comes, <u>she'll</u> give us our lunch. Uncle Fred has funny hats. Which one do you think <u>he'll</u> be wearing today?

Page 19: Circus Syllables

Page 20: Time for a Puzzle

							¹b	a	r	n
				²s		o			
				h		o			
		³l	o	o	k				
				r			⁴s		
			⁵s	t	a	r	t		
			o				a		
			r		⁶f	a	r		
⁷f	o	o	t		o				
					r				

Page 24: Consonant or Vowel?
An arrow.

Page 26: Punctuation
Do you have a hat? Can I have a sandwich? No! What do you want? It's a trick! What a mess! How does it work? Is it his or hers?